Gratitude

JOURNAL

A DAILY PRACTICE

Published in Ireland by
GET UP AND GO PUBLICATIONS LTD
Sligo, Ireland.
Email: info@getupandgodiary.com
www.getupandgodiary.com

Compiled by Eileen Forrestal
Graphic design by Nuala Redmond
Illustrations: dreamstime.com; shutterstock.com
Printed in Ireland by GPS Colour Graphics.

ISBN 978-1-910921-25-8

GetUpandGo

THERE IS ♥
always
something to be
THANKFUL FOR

Gratitude

Gratitude is an attitude and, like all attitudes, it is a choice. When we choose gratitude and choose to see the world through grateful eyes, we see an entirely different world. Gratitude is an expression of thankfulness for all that we are, and all that we have. It is also a thankfulness for all that we are not, and all that we do not have.

When we express gratitude authentically we acknowledge that we are truly present to receiving the gift that is being offered to us. When we express gratitude for our life, we are present to the gift that our life is – the opportunity to be alive. When we authentically express gratitude to others, they have the experience of being acknowledged, appreciated and valued, which is truly a profound gift to them.

In moments of gratitude we are called into the present, to where we are in our lives right now. In this moment we are mindful of who we are, what we have, the road we have travelled to get here and the unique opportunity that this moment brings.

In the spirit of true gratitude we can acknowledge the contribution that circumstances and individuals have made to our lives, and what they have made possible for us. We can now be grateful for each and every experience, every lesson, every choice, every decision, every action and every result.

In the spirit of gratitude we can reflect on the ground we have taken and the journey that is ahead.

Sometimes we forget, and take for granted that for which we were once so grateful. In the taking it for granted, we may sadly no longer be present to the gift that it is in our life now. We each have a choice – to view life as a gift and be grateful or to view life as a chore and be bitter.

The lens through which we choose to view our life will determine what we see. If we choose to wear shaded sunglasses, we must expect to have a dim view of the world.

Sometimes, viewing our life through the lens of gratitude is very challenging. It is not easy to be grateful when the world seems to be 'against us', when we, or loved ones, are ill, or leave us; when we are struggling with pain, sadness and loss; when we are faced with fear and uncertainty. Challenging as it is, the whole world is always at our feet, and the point of power is always in the present moment. When, in the midst of confusion and despair, we can still choose an attitude of gratitude and look for all we can be grateful for, a different world appears; an amazing place where anything is possible, where everything is perfect just as it is, and, whether we understand it or not, everything is unfolding exactly as it should.

In this journal we invite you to take time daily to explore and discover all that you can be grateful for in your own life. In doing this as a five-minute daily practice you will get present to the miracle that your life is, and not just your life, but the life of every living organism that we have the privilege of sharing this mysterious journey of life on earth.

This is your opportunity to get present to who you are as a loving human being, and to the opportunity that your life is to fulfil on what the world needs. You are a gift and your contribution is unique and valuable.

– *Eileen Forrestal*

No one can be grateful and unhappy at the same time.

This year, mend a quarrel. Seek out a forgotten friend. Dismiss suspicion and replace it with trust. Write a letter. Give a soft answer. Encourage youth. Manifest your loyalty in word and deed. Keep a promise. Forgo a grudge. Forgive an enemy. Apologise. Try to understand. Examine your demands on others. Think first of someone else. Be kind. Be gentle. Laugh a little more. Express your gratitude. Welcome a stranger. Gladden the heart of a child. Take pleasure in the beauty and wonder of the earth. Speak your love and then speak it again.

Benefits of Gratitude

Gratitude is a massively underutilised tool for improving life-satisfaction, happiness and overall health. A few minutes a day contemplating on gratitude will increase our long-term well-being.

Gratitude shifts our focus from what our life lacks to the abundance that is already present. We can start finding joy in the small things and appreciate simple pleasures.

Getting into the habit of daily gratitude exercises results in higher levels of satisfaction, optimism, and energy, and greater progress toward achieving personal goals.

Gratitude makes us happier

Practicing gratitude can increase happiness levels by around 25%. Gratitude makes us nicer, more trusting, more social, and more appreciative. As a result, it helps us make more friends and deepen and improve our existing relationships.

Expressing gratitude is not to say that everything in our lives is necessarily great. When things don't go our way, we can remember that within every difficulty lies the seeds of an equal or greater benefit. In the face of adversity we can ask ourselves "Is there anything here that I can be grateful for?"

Gratitude is a positive emotion

We tend to take for granted the good that is already present in our lives. There's a gratitude exercise that instructs us to imagine losing some of the things that we take for granted, such as our home, our ability to see or hear, our ability to walk, our friends, our health, or anything that currently gives us comfort. Then imagine getting each of these things back, one by one, and consider how grateful we would be for each and every one. Suddenly we can see the positives outweighing the negatives in our lives and a feeling of gratitude is inevitable.

Gratitude makes us healthier

Gratitude is a positive emotion strongly correlated with optimism. Positive emotions improve health. Optimism makes us happier, improves our health, and can been correlated with an overall more enjoyable experience of life.

Research has shown that those who practice gratitude tend to be more creative, bounce back more quickly from adversity, have a stronger immune system, and have stronger social relationships than those who don't practice gratitude.

Gratitude leads to increased feelings of well-being and relatedness, increased ability to appreciate and enjoy the good things in life.

If we want to improve our general health and well being, increase our level of happiness and satisfaction in life, and reduce the risk of detrimental thoughts and behaviour, focusing on gratitude is an important first step.

Gratitude encourages a positive mindset

Gratitude and vitality are strongly correlated. The more grateful we are, the more likely we are to celebrate our physical and mental wellbeing. Being grateful for our health would increase our desire to want to protect it. If we want to improve our health, we must adjust our mindset.

Benefits of a positive mindset include better coping with, and management of, chronic or terminal conditions, strengthening of our immune system functioning, faster recovery from illness or procedures, positive health behavior, having fewer complaints, lower blood pressure, and less likely to develop a stress, anxiety or depressive disorder.

Gratitude improves sleep

Thinking about and reflecting on a few things we can be grateful for at the end of the day, (instead of comparing ourselves with others or stressing about what we did or didn't get done), will induce a relaxation response, reducing the time required to fall asleep, and increasing quality and duration of sleep.

Today, you can start to let gratitude shine a light on your life that will soften your heart and open your mind, revealing truths that have been hidden from your view and leading you toward a richer, more joyful and more fulfilling life.

– Eileen Forrestal

Every morning we wake up with the same choice: What will my attitude be today? Ask yourself that without fail. Decide that no matter what the day brings, your attitude will include three elements: an awareness of how far you've come, gratitude for where you are, and determination to keep moving in the right direction.

Toni Sorenson

Reasons to be thankful this January:

January

In this new year, may you have a deep understanding of your true value and worth, an absolute faith in your unlimited potential, peace of mind in the midst of uncertainty, the confidence to let go when you need to, acceptance to replace your resistance, gratitude to open your heart, the strength to meet your challenges, great love to replace your fear, forgiveness and compassion for those who offend you, clear sight to see your best and true path, hope to dispel obscurity, the conviction to make your dreams come true, meaningful and rewarding synchronicities, dear friends who truly know and love you, a childlike trust in the benevolence of the universe, the humility to remain teachable, the wisdom to fully embrace your life exactly as it is, the understanding that every soul has its own course to follow, the discernment to recognise your own unique inner voice of truth, and the courage to learn to be still.

Janet Rebhan

JANUARY 1

JANUARY 2

JANUARY 3

JANUARY 4

Let us be grateful to the people who make us happy;
they are the charming gardeners who
make our souls blossom.

Marcel Proust

JANUARY **5**

JANUARY **6**

JANUARY **7**

JANUARY 8

JANUARY 9

JANUARY 10

*Walk as if you are kissing the
Earth with your feet.*

Thich Nhat Hanh

JANUARY **11**

JANUARY **12**

JANUARY **13**

JANUARY **14**

JANUARY **15**

JANUARY **16**

JANUARY **17**

JANUARY **18**

*We must find time to stop
and thank the people who make
a difference in our lives.*

John F Kennedy

JANUARY **19**

JANUARY **20**

JANUARY **21**

JANUARY **22**

JANUARY **23**

JANUARY **24**

*Wealth can also be that attitude of gratitude
with which we remind ourselves everyday
to count our blessings.*

Chris Gardner

JANUARY **25**

JANUARY **26**

JANUARY **27**

JANUARY **28**

JANUARY **29**

JANUARY **30**

JANUARY **31**

Feeling gratitude and
not expressing it is like wrapping
a present and not giving it.

William Arthur Ward

My January gratitude:

Reasons to be thankful this February:

True happiness is to enjoy the present, without anxious dependence upon the future, not to amuse ourselves with either hopes or fears but to rest satisfied with what we have, which is sufficient, for he that is so wants nothing. The greatest blessings of mankind are within us and within our reach. A wise man is content with his lot, whatever it may be, without wishing for what he has not.

Seneca

Gratitude unlocks the fullness of life. It turns what we have into enough, and more. It turns denial into acceptance, chaos to order, confusion to clarity. It can turn a meal into a feast, a house into a home, a stranger into a friend. Gratitude makes sense of our past, brings peace for today and creates a vision for tomorrow.

Melody Beattie

February

FEBRUARY 1

FEBRUARY 2

FEBRUARY 3

FEBRUARY 4

We take for granted
the very things that most
deserve our gratitude.

Cynthia Ozick

FEBRUARY **5**

FEBRUARY **6**

FEBRUARY **7**

FEBRUARY **8**

FEBRUARY **9**

FEBRUARY **10**

When we give cheerfully and accept
gratefully, everyone is blessed.

Maya Angelou

FEBRUARY 11

FEBRUARY 12

FEBRUARY 13

FEBRUARY 14

FEBRUARY **15**

FEBRUARY **16**

FEBRUARY **17**

FEBRUARY **18**

Gratitude bestows reverence, allowing us to encounter everyday epiphanies, those transcendent moments of awe that change forever how we experience life and the world.

Sarah Ban Breathnach

FEBRUARY 19

FEBRUARY 20

FEBRUARY 21

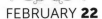

FEBRUARY **22**

FEBRUARY **23**

FEBRUARY **24**

Gratitude is a sign of maturity.
Where there is appreciation, there is also
courtesy and concern for the rights
and property of others.

Gordon B Hinckley

FEBRUARY **25**

....

....

....

....

....

FEBRUARY **26**

....

....

....

....

....

FEBRUARY **27**

....

....

....

....

....

FEBRUARY **28**

....

....

....

....

....

Although time seems to fly, it never travels faster than one day at a time. Each day is a new opportunity to live your life to the fullest. In each waking day, you will find scores of blessings and opportunities for positive change. Do not let your today be stolen by the unchangeable past or the indefinite future! Today is a new day!

Steve Maraboli

NOTHING IS MORE

Honorable

···· THAN A ····

GRATEFUL
HEART

FEBRUARY **29**

My February gratitude:

The world is so exquisite with so much love and moral depth, that there is no reason to deceive ourselves with pretty stories for which there's little good evidence. Far better it seems to me, in our vulnerability, is to look death in the eye and to be grateful every day for the brief but magnificent opportunity that life provides.

Carl Sagan

Reasons to be thankful this March:

March

DARE TO BE

When a new day begins, dare to smile gratefully. When there is darkness, dare to be the first to shine a light. When there is injustice, dare to be the first to condemn it. When something seems difficult, dare to do it anyway. When life seems to beat you down, dare to fight back. When there seems to be no hope, dare to find some. When you're feeling tired, dare to keep going. When times are tough, dare to be tougher. When love hurts you, dare to love again. When someone is hurting, dare to help them heal. When another is lost, dare to help them find the way. When a friend falls, dare to be the first to extend a hand. When you cross paths with another, dare to make them smile. When you feel great, dare to help someone else feel great too. When the day has ended, dare to feel as you've done your best. Dare to be the best you can. At all times, Dare to be!

Steve Maraboli

MARCH **1**

MARCH **2**

MARCH **3**

MARCH **4**

Do not spoil what you have by desiring what you have not; remember that what you now have was once among the things you only hoped for.

Epicurus

MARCH **5**

MARCH **6**

MARCH **7**

MARCH **8**

MARCH **9**

MARCH **10**

You pray in your distress and in your need;
would that you might pray also in the fullness of your
joy and in your days of abundance.

Kahlil Gibran

MARCH 11

MARCH 12

MARCH 13

MARCH 14

MARCH **15**

MARCH **16**

MARCH **17**

MARCH **18**

Happiness is the spiritual experience of living every minute with love, grace, and gratitude.

Denis Waitley

MARCH **19**

MARCH **20**

MARCH **21**

MARCH **22**

MARCH **23**

MARCH **24**

*At times our own light goes out and is rekindled
by a spark from another person. Each of us has cause
to think with deep gratitude of those who have
lighted the flame within us.*

Albert Schweitzer

MARCH 25

MARCH 26

MARCH 27

MARCH 28

MARCH **29**

MARCH **30**

MARCH **31**

Gratitude can transform common days into thanksgivings, turn routine jobs into joy, and change ordinary opportunities into blessings.

William Arthur Ward

My March gratitude:

Reasons to be thankful this April:

Gratitude is the beginning of civility, of decency and goodness, of a recognition that we cannot afford to be arrogant. We should walk with the knowledge that we will need help every step of the way.

Gordon B Hinckley

Every person has the power to make others happy. Some do it simply by entering a room others by leaving the room. Some individuals leave trails of gloom; others, trails of joy. Some leave trails of hate and bitterness; others, trails of love and harmony. Some leave trails of cynicism and pessimism; others trails of faith and optimism. Some leave trails of criticism and resignation; others trails of gratitude and hope. What kind of trails do you leave?

William Arthur Ward

April

APRIL 1

APRIL 2

APRIL 3

APRIL 4

*We can complain because rose bushes
have thorns, or rejoice because
thorns have roses.*

Alphonse Karr

APRIL **5**

APRIL **6**

APRIL **7**

APRIL **8**

APRIL **9**

APRIL **10**

*Showing gratitude is one of the
simplest yet most powerful things
humans can do for each other.*

Randy Pausch

APRIL **11**

APRIL **12**

APRIL **13**

APRIL **14**

APRIL **15**

APRIL **16**

APRIL **17**

APRIL **18**

The most fortunate are those who have a wonderful capacity to appreciate again and again, freshly and naively, the basic goods of life, with awe, pleasure, wonder and even ecstasy.

Abraham H Maslow

APRIL **19**

APRIL **20**

APRIL **21**

APRIL **22**

APRIL **23**

APRIL **24**

One minute of sincere gratitude can wash away a lifetime's disappointments.

Silvia Hartmann

APRIL **25**

APRIL **26**

APRIL **27**

APRIL **28**

*If you concentrate on finding whatever is good
in every situation, you will discover that your life
will suddenly be filled with gratitude,
a feeling that nurtures the soul.*

Harold S Kushner

My April gratitude:

Take full account of what excellencies you possess, and in gratitude remember how you would hanker after them, if you had them not.

Marcus Aurelius

Reasons to be thankful this May:

May

To educate yourself for the feeling of gratitude means to take nothing for granted, but to always seek out and value the kind that will stand behind the action. Nothing that is done for you is a matter of course. Everything originates in a will for the good, which is directed at you. Train yourself never to put off the word or action for the expression of gratitude.

Albert Schweitzer

MAY **1**

MAY **2**

MAY **3**

MAY **4**

*True forgiveness is when you can say
'thank you for that experience'.*

Oprah Winfrey

MAY **5**

MAY **6**

MAY **7**

MAY **8**

MAY **9**

MAY **10**

Appreciation is a wonderful thing.
It makes what is excellent in others
belong to us as well.

Voltaire

MAY 11

MAY 12

MAY 13

MAY 14

MAY 15

MAY 16

MAY 17

MAY 18

Gratitude is the sweetest thing in a seeker's life –
in all human life. If there is gratitude in your
heart, then there will be tremendous
sweetness in your eyes.

Sri Chinmoy

MAY **19**

MAY **20**

MAY **21**

MAY **22**

MAY **23**

MAY **24**

Breath is the finest gift of nature.
Be grateful for this wonderful gift.

Amit Ray

MAY 25

MAY 26

MAY 27

MAY 28

MAY **29**

MAY **30**

MAY **31**

*The way to move out of judgement
is to move into gratitude.*

Neale Donald Walsch

My May gratitude:

Reasons to be thankful this June:

For we are all amateurs at life, but if we do not focus too much on our mistakes, a miraculous picture emerges. And we learn that it's not the beauty of the image that warrants our gratitude – it's the chance to paint.

Richard Paul Evans

Unless you start feeling the source of light within yourself, you will not be able to see that light anywhere else. First it has to be experienced within one's own being, then it is found everywhere. Then the whole existence becomes so full of light, so full of joy, so full of meaning and poetry, that each moment one feels grateful for all that god has given, for all that he goes on giving. Once it is found, once you are centered, once you are bathed in your own light you have a different vision, a different perspective, and the whole of life becomes golden. Then even dust is divine. Then life is so rich, so abundantly rich that one can only feel a tremendous gratitude towards existence. That gratitude becomes prayer. Before that, all prayer is false.

Osho

June

JUNE **1**

JUNE **2**

JUNE **3**

JUNE **4**

Cultivate the habit of being grateful for every good thing that comes to you, and to give thanks continuously. And because all things have contributed to your advancement, you should include all things in your gratitude.

Ralph Waldo Emerson

JUNE **5**

JUNE **6**

JUNE **7**

JUNE **8**

JUNE **9**

JUNE **10**

Gratitude is not only the greatest of virtues,
but the parent of all others.

Marcus Tullius Cicero

JUNE 11

JUNE 12

JUNE 13

JUNE 14

JUNE **15**

JUNE **16**

JUNE **17**

JUNE **18**

*Learn to be thankful for
what you already have, while you
pursue all that you want.*

Jim Rohn

JUNE **19**

JUNE **20**

JUNE **21**

JUNE 22

JUNE 23

JUNE 24

*Enjoy the little things, for one day
you may look back and realise they
were the big things.*

Robert Brault

JUNE 25

JUNE 26

JUNE 27

JUNE 28

JUNE **29**

_____

_____

_____

_____

_____

JUNE **30**

_____

_____

_____

_____

_____

Give yourself a gift of five minutes of
contemplation in awe of everything you see around
you. Go outside and turn your attention to the many
miracles around you. This five-minute-a-day
regimen of appreciation and gratitude will
help you to focus your life in awe.

Wayne Dyer

My June gratitude:

Then comes hope with a smile and whispers, 'there is joy is self-forgetfulness.' So I try to make the light in others' eyes my sun, the music in others' ears my symphony, the smile on others' lips my happiness.

Helen Keller

Reasons to be thankful this July:

July

I will live this day as if it is my last. I will waste not a moment mourning yesterday's misfortunes, yesterday's defeats, yesterday's aches of the heart, for why should I throw good after bad?" I will live this day as if it is my last. This day is all I have and these hours are now my eternity. I greet this sunrise with cries of joy as a prisoner who is reprieved from death. I lift mine arms with thanks for this priceless gift of a new day. So too, I will beat upon my heart with gratitude as I consider all who greeted yesterday's sunrise who are no longer with the living today. I am indeed a fortunate man and today's hours are but a bonus, undeserved. Why have I been allowed to live this extra day when others, far better than I, have departed? Is it that they have accomplished their purpose while mine is yet to be achieved? Is this another opportunity for me to become the man I know I can be?

Og Mandino

JULY **1**

JULY **2**

JULY **3**

JULY **4**

Piglet noticed that even though he had a very small heart, it could hold a rather large amount of gratitude.

AA Milne

JULY **5**

JULY **6**

JULY **7**

JULY **8**

JULY **9**

JULY **10**

As we express our gratitude, we must never forget that the highest appreciation is not to utter words, but to live by them.

John F Kennedy

JULY **11**

JULY **12**

JULY **13**

JULY **14**

JULY **15**

JULY **16**

JULY **17**

JULY **18**

Because all things have contributed to your advancement, you should include all things in your gratitude.

Wallace D Wattles

JULY **19**

JULY **20**

JULY **21**

JULY **22**

JULY **23**

JULY **24**

May I live this day compassionate of heart,
clear in word, gracious in awareness, courageous
in thought, generous in love.

John O'Donohue

JULY **25**

JULY **26**

JULY **27**

JULY **28**

JULY **29**

JULY **30**

JULY **31**

*Act with kindness, but do
not expect gratitude.*

Confucius

My July gratitude:

Reasons to be thankful this August:

Being in the habit of saying 'thank you', of making sure that people receive attention so they know you value them, of not presuming that people will always be there – this is a good habit, regardless – make sure to give virtual and actual high-fives to those who rock and rock hard.

Sarah Wendell

An understanding heart is everything in a teacher, and cannot be esteemed highly enough. One looks back with appreciation to the brilliant teachers, but with gratitude to those who touched our human feeling. The curriculum is so much necessary raw material, but warmth is the vital element for the growing plant and for the soul of the child.

CG Jung

August

AUGUST **1**

AUGUST **2**

AUGUST **3**

AUGUST **4**

When I started counting my blessings,
my whole life turned around.

Willie Nelson

AUGUST 5

AUGUST 6

AUGUST 7

AUGUST 8

AUGUST 9

AUGUST 10

The roots of all goodness lie in the soil
of appreciation for goodness.

Dalai Lama

AUGUST 11

AUGUST 12

AUGUST 13

AUGUST 14

AUGUST **15**

AUGUST **16**

AUGUST **17**

AUGUST **18**

*When it comes to life, the critical thing
is whether you take things for granted
or take them with gratitude.*

GK Chesterton

AUGUST **19**

AUGUST **20**

AUGUST **21**

AUGUST 22

AUGUST 23

AUGUST 24

I may not be where I want to be,
but I'm thankful for not being
where I used to be.

Habeeb Akande

AUGUST **25**

AUGUST **26**

AUGUST **27**

AUGUST **28**

AUGUST **29**

AUGUST **30**

AUGUST **31**

There are only two ways to live your life.
One is as though nothing is a miracle. The other
is as though everything is a miracle.

Albert Einstein

My August gratitude:

Gratitude is the beginning of wisdom. Stated differently, true wisdom cannot be obtained unless it is built on a foundation of true humility and gratitude.

Gordon B Hinckley

Reasons to be thankful this September:

September

When I look back upon my early days I am stirred by the thought of the number of people whom I have to thank for what they gave me or for what they were to me. At the same time I am haunted by an oppressive consciousness of the little gratitude I really showed them while I was young. How many of them have said farewell to life without having made clear to them what it meant to me to receive from them so much kindness or so much care! Many a time have I, with a feeling of shame, said quietly to myself over a grave the words which my mouth ought to have spoken to the departed, while he was still in the flesh.

Albert Schweitzer

SEPTEMBER **1**

SEPTEMBER **2**

SEPTEMBER **3**

SEPTEMBER **4**

I would maintain that thanks is the highest form of thought; and that gratitude is happiness doubled by wonder.

GK Chesterton

SEPTEMBER **5**

SEPTEMBER **6**

SEPTEMBER **7**

SEPTEMBER 8

SEPTEMBER 9

SEPTEMBER 10

Free yourself from the complexities and drama of your life. Simplify. Look within. Within ourselves we all have the gifts and talents we need to fulfill the purpose we've been blessed with.

Steve Maraboli

SEPTEMBER **11**

SEPTEMBER **12**

SEPTEMBER **13**

SEPTEMBER **14**

SEPTEMBER **15**

SEPTEMBER **16**

SEPTEMBER **17**

SEPTEMBER **18**

It is through gratitude for the present moment that the spiritual dimension of life opens up.

Eckhart Tolle

SEPTEMBER **19**

SEPTEMBER **20**

SEPTEMBER **21**

SEPTEMBER **22**

SEPTEMBER **23**

SEPTEMBER **24**

*The way to develop the best that is in a person is
by appreciation and encouragement.*

Charles Schwab

SEPTEMBER **25**

SEPTEMBER **26**

SEPTEMBER **27**

SEPTEMBER **28**

SEPTEMBER **29**

SEPTEMBER **30**

*Keeping your body healthy
is an expression of gratitude to
the whole cosmos – the trees,
the clouds, everything.*

Thich Nhat Hanh

My September gratitude:

Reasons to be thankful this October:

But then, a grateful heart beats in a world of miracles. If I could only speak one prayer for you, my children, it would be that your hearts would not only beat but grow ever greater in gratitude, that your lives, however long they prove to be and no matter how they end, continue to bring you miracles in abundance.

Kate Braestrup

Without darkness, we may never know how bright the stars shine. Without battles, we could not know what victory feels like. Without adversity, we may never appreciate the abundance in our lives. Be thankful, not only for the easy times, but for every experience that has made you who you are.

Julie-Anne

October

OCTOBER **1**

OCTOBER **2**

OCTOBER **3**

OCTOBER **4**

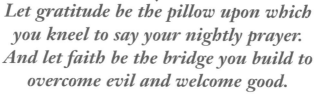

Let gratitude be the pillow upon which
you kneel to say your nightly prayer.
And let faith be the bridge you build to
overcome evil and welcome good.

Maya Angelou

OCTOBER **5**

OCTOBER **6**

OCTOBER **7**

OCTOBER **8**

OCTOBER **9**

OCTOBER **10**

May you experience each day as a sacred gift
woven around the heart of wonder.

John O'Donohue

OCTOBER **11**

OCTOBER **12**

OCTOBER **13**

OCTOBER **14**

OCTOBER 15

OCTOBER 16

OCTOBER 17

OCTOBER 18

*Gratitude makes sense of our past,
brings peace for today, and creates a
vision for tomorrow.*

Melody Beattie

OCTOBER **19**

OCTOBER **20**

OCTOBER **21**

OCTOBER **22**

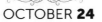

OCTOBER **23**

OCTOBER **24**

*Sometimes we should express our gratitude
for the small and simple things like the scent
of the rain, the taste of your favorite food,
or the sound of a loved one's voice.*

Joseph B Wirthlin

OCTOBER **25**

OCTOBER **26**

OCTOBER **27**

OCTOBER **28**

OCTOBER **29**

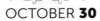

OCTOBER **30**

OCTOBER **31**

I have noticed that the universe loves gratitude. The more grateful you are, the more goodies you get.

Louise L Hay

My October gratitude:

It has been said that life has treated me harshly; and sometimes I have complained in my heart because many pleasures of human experience have been withheld from me – if much has been denied me, much, very much, has been given me.

Helen Keller

Reasons to be thankful this November:

November

Gratitude means to recognise the good in your life, be thankful for whatever you have, some people may not even have one of those things you consider precious to you (love, family, friends etc). Each day give thanks for the gift of life. You are blessed.

Pablo

NOVEMBER **1**

NOVEMBER **2**

NOVEMBER **3**

NOVEMBER **4**

Acknowledging the good that you already have in your life is the foundation for all abundance.

Eckhart Tolle

NOVEMBER 5

NOVEMBER 6

NOVEMBER 7

NOVEMBER **8**

NOVEMBER **9**

NOVEMBER **10**

When we can do nothing else,
we can still love, without expecting any
reward or change or gratitude.

Paulo Coelho

NOVEMBER 11

NOVEMBER 12

NOVEMBER 13

NOVEMBER 14

NOVEMBER **15**

NOVEMBER **16**

NOVEMBER **17**

NOVEMBER **18**

Reflect upon your present blessings,
of which every man has plenty;
not on your past misfortunes,
of which all men have some.

Charles Dickens

NOVEMBER 19

NOVEMBER 20

NOVEMBER 21

NOVEMBER **22**

NOVEMBER **23**

NOVEMBER **24**

None is more impoverished than the one who has no gratitude. Gratitude is a currency that we can mint for ourselves, and spend without fear of bankruptcy.

Fred De Witt Van Amburgh

NOVEMBER **25**

NOVEMBER **26**

NOVEMBER **27**

NOVEMBER **28**

NOVEMBER 29

NOVEMBER 30

May dawn find you awake and alert, approaching your
new day with dreams, possibilities and promises;
May evening find you gracious and fulfilled;
May you go into the night blessed, sheltered and protected;
May your soul calm, console and renew you.

John O'Donohue

My November gratitude:

Reasons to be thankful this December:

⁂

The greatest wisdom is in simplicity. Love, respect, tolerance, sharing, gratitude, forgiveness. It's not complex or elaborate. The real knowledge is free. It's encoded in your DNA. All you need is within you. Great teachers have said that from the beginning. Find your heart, and you will find your way.

Carlos Barrios

There will be no one like us when we are gone, but then there is no one like anyone else, ever. When people die, they cannot be replaced. They leave holes that cannot be filled, for it is the fate – the genetic and neural fate – of every human being to be a unique individual, to find his own path, to live his own life, to die his own death. I cannot pretend I am without fear. But my predominant feeling is one of gratitude. I have loved and been loved; I have been given much and I have given something in return; Above all, I have been a sentient being, a thinking animal, on this beautiful planet, and that in itself has been an enormous privilege and adventure.

Oliver Sacks

December

DECEMBER **1**

DECEMBER **2**

DECEMBER **3**

DECEMBER **4**

If the only prayer you said was thank you,
that would be enough.

Meister Eckhart

DECEMBER **5**

DECEMBER **6**

DECEMBER **7**

DECEMBER **8**

DECEMBER **9**

DECEMBER **10**

*You will never accept gratitude as a solution
to your problems, until you have reached
the last stage of grief – acceptance.*

Shannon L Alder

DECEMBER 11

DECEMBER 12

DECEMBER 13

DECEMBER 14

DECEMBER **15**

DECEMBER **16**

DECEMBER **17**

DECEMBER **18**

The unthankful heart discovers no mercies;
but the thankful heart will find, in every hour,
some heavenly blessings.

Henry Ward Beecher

DECEMBER **19**

DECEMBER **20**

DECEMBER **21**

DECEMBER **22**

DECEMBER **23**

DECEMBER **24**

In an expression of true gratitude,
sadness is conspicuous only by its absence.

Marcus Aurelius

DECEMBER **25**

DECEMBER **26**

DECEMBER **27**

DECEMBER **28**

DECEMBER **29**

DECEMBER **30**

DECEMBER **31**

Gratitude is looking on the brighter side of life, even if it means hurting your eyes.

Ellen DeGeneres

My December gratitude:

Blessed be the gifts you never notice, your health, eyes to behold the world, thoughts to countenance the unknown, memory to harvest vanished days, your heart to feel the world's waves, your breath to breathe the nourishment of distance made intimate by earth.

John O'Donohue

Develop an attitude of gratitude, and give thanks for everything that happens to you, knowing that every step forward is a step toward achieving something bigger and better than your current situation.

Brian Tracy

When you know in your bones that your body is a sacred gift, you move in the world with an effortless grace. Gratitude and humility rise up spontaneously.

Debbie Ford

Desiderata

Go placidly amid the noise and haste, and remember what peace
there may be in silence. As far as possible without surrender be on
good terms with all persons. Speak your truth quietly and clearly, and
listen to others, even the dull and ignorant; they too have their story.

Avoid loud and aggressive persons, they are vexations to the spirit.
If you compare yourself with others, you may become vain and bitter;
for always there will be greater and lesser persons than yourself. Enjoy
your achievements as well as your plans. Keep interested in your own
career, however humble; it is a real possession in the changing fortunes
of time. Exercise caution in your business affairs; for the world is full of
trickery. But let this not blind you to what virtue there is; many persons
strive for high ideals; and everywhere life is full of heroism.

Be yourself. Especially, do not feign affection. Neither be cynical
about love; for in the face of all aridity and disenchantment it is
perennial as the grass. Take kindly the counsel of the years,
gracefully surrendering the things of youth. Nurture strength
of spirit to shield you in sudden misfortune. But do not distress
yourself with imaginings. Many fears are born of fatigue and
loneliness. Beyond a wholesome discipline, be gentle with yourself.

You are a child of the universe, no less than the trees and the stars;
you have a right to be here. And whether or not it is clear to you, no
doubt the universe is unfolding as it should. Therefore be at peace
with God, whatever you conceive Him to be; and whatever your
labours and aspirations, in the noisy confusion of life keep peace
with your soul. With all its sham, drudgery and broken dreams,
it is still a beautiful world. Be cheerful. Strive to be happy.

Max Ehrmann

VISIT OUR WEBSITE

www.getupandgodiary.com

OR CONTACT US ON
info@getupandgodiary.com